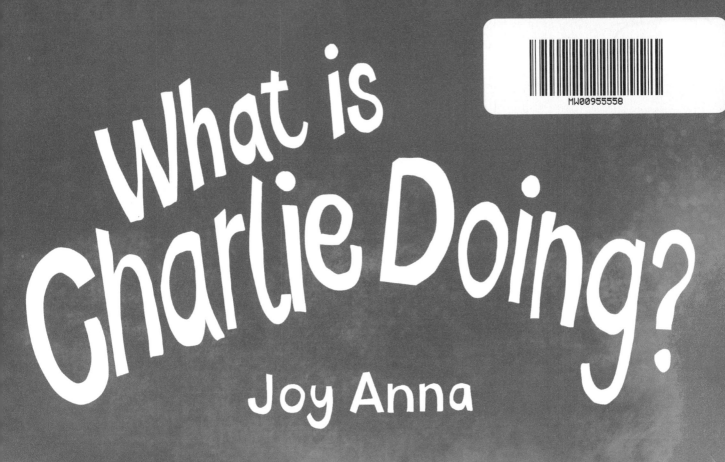

What is Charlie Doing?

Joy Anna

Illustrated by
Noah Warnes

Illustrated by Noah Warnes
Cover Design, Typography and Formatting
by Noah Warnes
Editing by Stacey Smekofske, editsbystacey.com

ISBN: 978-1-952123-02-3 (paperback)
ISBN: 978-1-952123-04-7 (hardback)
ISBN: 978-1-952123-03-0 (ebook)

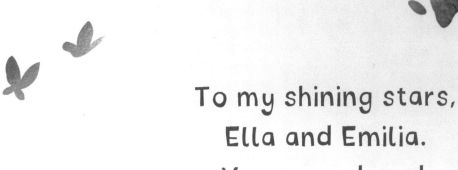

To my shining stars,
Ella and Emilia.
You are adored.
You bring light and hope
to a fallen world.
You were created for a purpose.
The sky is not the limit,
so don't be afraid to reach for it.
I believe in you.
You leave sparkles wherever you go.
Nana loves you forever.

My name
is Charlie.
I am a
Goldendoodle.

I was born on a farm
and had eight
brothers and sisters.

I was the only chocolate
puppy
in my entire litter.
I was the biggest
puppy in my litter.

My mommy's name is Brook.
My daddy's name is Rags.
I was a cute puppy.
I was born with a special nose.
I use my nose to help humans.

My unique nose is up to 100,000 times stronger than my human's nose.

I learned that different smells mean different things for my human.

There are happy scents.

There are angry scents.

There are
fear
scents.

There are disgusting scents.

There are
Surprise scents.

Each of these scents is unique.

Using my nose, my job is to help my human, Joy.

I learned how to let her know when I detect a scary scent.

I had to learn what each of these scents smells like on my human by spending time with her.

I let my human know when I detect a scary scent by standing still, placing my head on her lap, or lying against her to make her stay still. She needs me.

I stay with my human when I detect a scary scent, and I bark to get her attention to help if she needs it.

While I had to learn how to use my nose, I had to learn other things, too.

I had to learn how to go upstairs. The loud metal ones were hard and slippery, but I did it.

I had to learn how to ride in a car with a seat belt and sit still. I had to learn not to be scared of loud noises that might startle me.

I had to learn to sit still in places that are small and awkward like skinny metal benches or crowded and loud places like airplanes, trams, or subways.

I wear a red vest in public so everyone can see that I have a job and that I am working. When I am working, you should not touch me. My human reminds people not to touch me when they see me, so I can do my job.

Touching me will distract me from my job with my human.

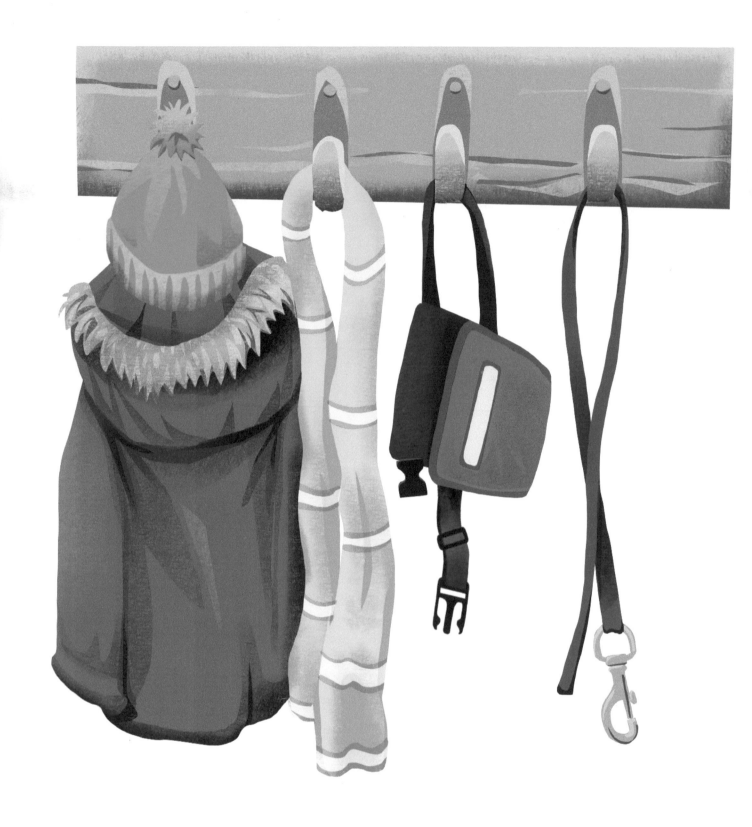

When I'm done working in public, my vest comes off and I look like every other dog, but I keep working.

The next time you see a
service dog with a red vest on,
please don't touch them.
They are working hard.
Let them do their job;
their human's life depends on it.

I love Joy, and helping her is a great job.

I love my job as a service dog.

MOM. I love you, and miss you so much. I can't help but feel you looking over my shoulder when I am clanking away on your typewriter. I can hear you correcting my English, you were the original Grammar Police and I am forever thankful. I know you are proud of me.

DAD. Thank you for your faith, which is my foundation. You are the writer in our family. Your sense of wit, your way with words, I inherited that from you. My favorite "Dad Sea Scrolls," are priceless. I know you miss your angel dearly, but I am thankful I have had these past few years to love on you, laugh so hard and spend time with my Daddio. Your favorite daughter loves you so much.

To my village of girlfriends. You know who you are, and I love you, each of you, fiercely, independently, and loyally. Each of you is a Godsend, unique and a lifesaver. I would not be here today if it weren't for your love, support, and encouragement. Thank you.

To my Editor Stacey, you are just what I need. Raw, honest, plodding, blunt, no fear, risk-taker, professional, humorous, and extremely patient. Thank you for knowing when I need encouragement or when I need a thump.

To Charlie, you are the perfect example of earthly unconditional love. You serve me without complaint, with excellence, watch over me during some of my darkest days, and have saved my life. You are family.

To my fans, you guys ROCK!!! I can't tell you how humbling your support is to me. How blessed I feel that you receive what I write with open hearts and minds. Thank you for understanding how eclectic I am and don't care that I don't follow the rules of a typical writer sticking to one genre. Thank you for your notes, texts, emails, social media posts of every kind, for asking for photos, autographs; it blows me away. Please know that I am thankful, grateful and blessed to be given this opportunity to write and so thankful for your belief in me. Thank you.

Thanks be to God, for without Him I am nothing.

ACKNOWLEDGMENTS FROM CHARLIE:

Thank you Nate, you showed me how to harness my excitement when my nose gives me the alarm and how to mind my manners in public. Thank you for teaching my mom and brother how to communicate with me.

Thank you Velinda and Janelle at Clip-N-Tails for keeping me purdy since I was a puppy. To Cassie for the in-betweeners.

Kisses to Dr. Brian Hewitt over at Cheyenne West Animal Hospital—thank you for keeping me healthy.

I am a loved, lucky and spoiled boy. You can connect with me on Instagram @Chuckthegoldendoodle1.

Woof. Woof. Lick. Lick, Charlie

Joy Anna was raised on a farm, she also lived outside the United States and was raised with all brothers. She loves Mondays, dislikes Fridays, loves skinny French Fries, Twizzlers, cheese, pickles and olives. She loves to write, doodle, landscape, garden and run. She is also a survivor and a woman of tremendous faith.

She has stores of energy that seem endless at times. She published her first book, *Just Joshin' Ya* with her third book coming soon. She has three kids and two granddaughters and lives in a warm house with her family and Charlie, her Goldendoodle.

You can connect with her on Facebook and Instagram:
🅕 🅘 @authorJoyanna

Or on her website:
www.AuthorJoyanna.com.

Noah Warnes lives in the south of England near the coast. He loves drawing in his sketchbook, painting, printmaking, playing the drums, and making stories come to life. You can find more of Noah's work at www.noahwarnes.com.

CPSIA information can be obtained
at www.ICGtesting.com
Printed in the USA
BVHW021936250621
610446BV00009B/297